Missa Cantata

A Chant Mass for the Assembly

(With Choir or Cantor)

**Accompaniments by
Geoffrey Cox**

The English Translation
of the Roman Missal (2010)

CATHOLIC TRUTH SOCIETY

PUBLISHERS TO THE HOLY SEE

Published by
THE CATHOLIC TRUTH SOCIETY
40-46 Harleyford Road, London, SE11 5AY

website: www.cts-online.org.uk

ISBN 978 1 86082 755 6

Contents

Preface

In preparing the English translation of *The Roman Missal* (2010), based on the *Missale Romanum, editio typical tertia* (2002), the International Commission on English in the Liturgy (ICEL) has simultaneously made available English adaptations of all the chant that is provided in the *Missale Romanum*.

While most of this chant is intended to be sung by the liturgical ministers, the *Missale Romanum* also includes some parts (such as the *Kyrie, Sanctus, Agnus Dei* and Lord's Prayer) that are sung by the entire assembly. In addition to these, ICEL has provided complete musical settings in English of the *Gloria* and *Credo*, which are not normally found in the Missal itself. The English translation of *The Roman Missal* (2010) thus provides music for all the parts of the Mass Ordinary that can be sung by the assembly.

Alongside the English adaptations of chant melodies made by ICEL, the new English translation retains the original Latin versions of the *Sanctus, Agnus Dei* and Lord's Prayer, and the Greek version of the *Kyrie*. This is in line with the expectation that, alongside the vernacular, "the faithful may also be able to say or sing together in Latin those parts of the Ordinary of the Mass which pertain to them" (Second Vatican Council, Constitution on the Sacred Liturgy *Sacrosanctum Concilium*, 1963, para. 54).

Chant melodies are traditionally sung without instrumental accompaniment, but the practice has developed of using organ or keyboard accompaniment for some of the parts sung by the assembly. This serves to support the singing, and thus to encourage "full and active participation by all the people" (Second Vatican Council, Constitution on the Sacred Liturgy *Sacrosanctum Concilium*, 1963, para. 113).

The present volume provides accompaniments for the main chants in the Missal that are intended to be sung by the assembly. For the sake of completeness, it also provides accompaniments for Gloria VIII and Credo III in Latin. Short dialogues between the celebrant and the assembly (such as in the Introductory Rites, the Preface Dialogue of the Eucharistic Prayer and in the Concluding Rites) are not provided here with accompaniment, and it is recommended that these be sung unaccompanied.

All of the chants in the present volume can be sung without accompaniment. It is hoped, however, that the provision of accompaniments will serve to encourage the continuing use of these Gregorian melodies, which represent a 'core repertory' for the assembly in singing the Mass. The melodies themselves provide a living connection between the new English texts and the Latin tradition of the Roman Rite.

Geoffrey Cox
Melbourne, August 2011.

Notes on Performance
and on the Musical Notation

The chant melodies are notated here, as in the English translation of *The Roman Missal* (2010), using the modern five-line stave with stemless note-heads. This is intended to encourage a natural accentuation of the texts, rather than a strictly 'rhythmic' interpretation.

The accompaniments are similarly intended to support the natural accentuation of the texts, and a non-rhythmic notation has been employed (modelled on that used in the German liturgical songbook *Gotteslob*), using 'open notes' of indeterminate value. The organist / keyboard player is thus required to follow the flow of the melody, rather than reading strict note values.

In view of the use of 'open notes' in the accompaniments, and in order to avoid confusion, dots and occasional episemas have been added (in the older tradition of Solesmes, and as in current Vatican usage) to indicate the recommended slight lengthening of some notes, especially at the ends of phrases.

The *Gloria* and *Credo* may be sung by the assembly throughout, or in *alternatim*. The *alternatim* practice is indicated here with sections marked '**C**' for the choir or cantor, and sections marked '**A**' for the assembly. The opening phrase is normally intoned by the celebrant or, if more convenient, by the cantor. *Alternatim* practice can be applied also to the *Kyrie,* as shown.

In the *Sanctus*, especially when sung without accompaniment, the cantor may sing alone up to the first quarter bar, joined by the assembly thereafter. Similarly if the *Agnus Dei* is sung without accompaniment, the cantor may sing the opening words of each invocation. When accompaniment is used, however, it should be possible for the entire assembly to sing these chants throughout, provided that the opening phrase is first played on the organ (preferably in unison). This practice of introducing chants on the organ may also be applied to the Memorial Acclamations.

The chants are presented here at a normative pitch for singing, but they may be transposed up or down as needed. When accompanying the cantor, the accompaniment should be kept light, and the melody line need not be doubled in the accompaniment if the cantor is confident.

Accompaniment on the organ should generally be light, on manuals only for the parts marked 'C' for the choir or cantor. When supporting the singing of the assembly, however, the accompaniment should be strengthened (including the use of the pedals on the organ), but it should never dominate.

Geoffrey Cox
Melbourne, August 2011.

Kyrie XVI

(Greek)

Melody: 11th-13th century

Accompaniment by
Geoffrey Cox

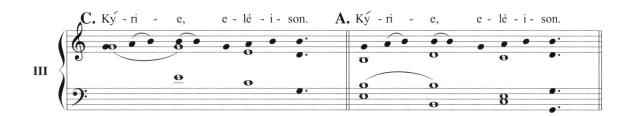

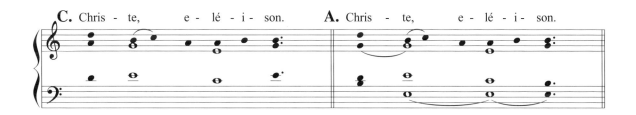

or

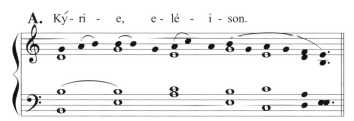

1

Kyrie XVI
(English)

Text and melody: ICEL

Accompaniment by
Geoffrey Cox

C. Lord, have mer - cy. **A.** Lord, have mer - cy.

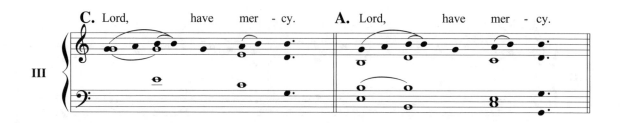

C. Christ, have mer - cy. **A.** Christ, have mer - cy.

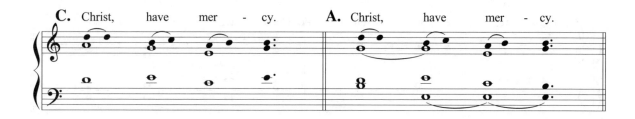

C. Lord, have mer - cy. **A.** Lord, have mer - cy.

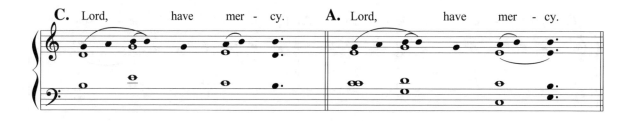

Gloria VIII
(Latin)

Melody: 16th century

Accompaniment by
Geoffrey Cox

Gló -ri - a in ex -cél -sis De - o. **C.** Et in ter -ra pax ho - mí -ni - bus

bo -nae vo -lun -tá -tis. **A.** Lau -dá - mus te. **C.** Be -ne -dí -ci -mus te.

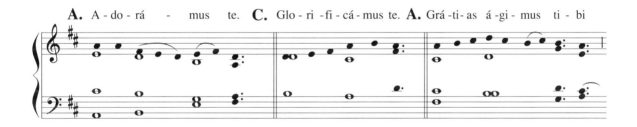

A. A -do -rá - mus te. **C.** Glo -ri -fi -cá -mus te. **A.** Grá -ti -as á -gi - mus ti - bi

pro -pter ma -gnam gló -ri -am tu -am. **C.** Dó - mi -ne De -us, Rex cae -lé - stis,

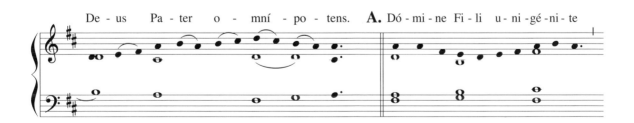

De -us Pa -ter o -mní -po -tens. **A.** Dó -mi -ne Fi -li u -ni -gé -ni -te

3

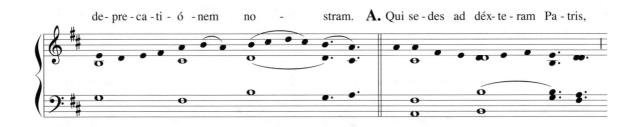

4

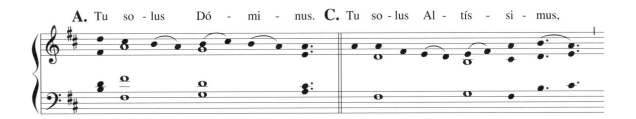

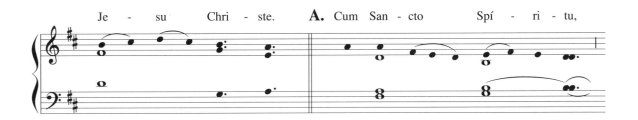

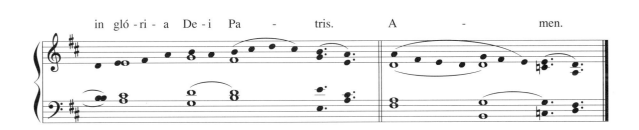

Gloria XV

(English)

Text and Melody: ICEL

Accompaniment by
Geoffrey Cox

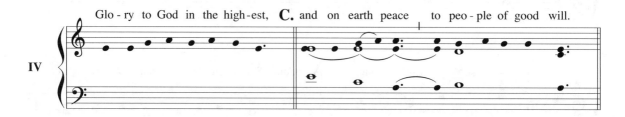

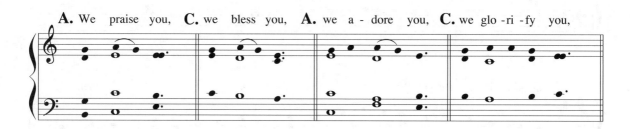

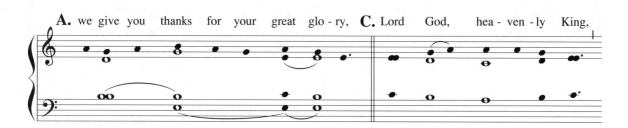

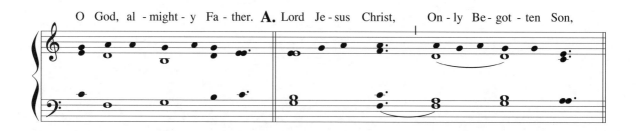

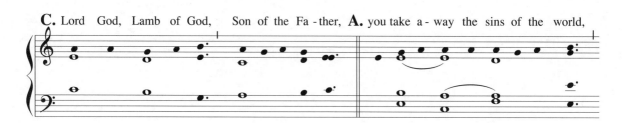

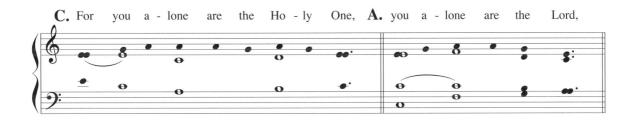

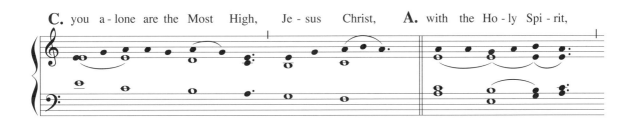

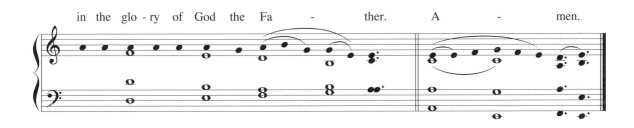

Credo I

(English)

Text and melody: ICEL

Accompaniment by
Geoffrey Cox

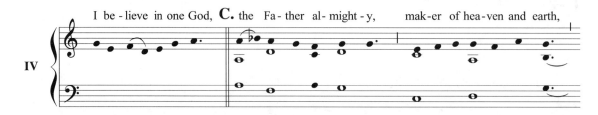

I be - lieve in one God, **C.** the Fa - ther al - might - y, mak-er of hea-ven and earth,

of all things vi - si - ble and in - vi - si - ble.

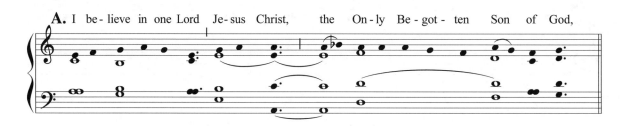

A. I be - lieve in one Lord Je - sus Christ, the On - ly Be - got - ten Son of God,

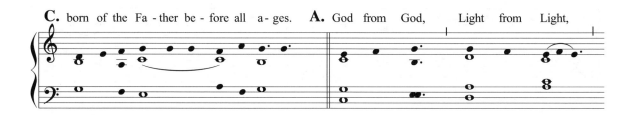

C. born of the Fa - ther be - fore all a - ges. **A.** God from God, Light from Light,

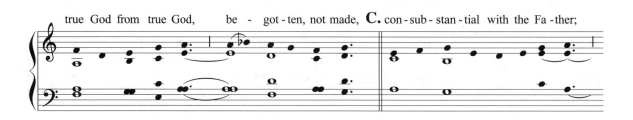

true God from true God, be - got - ten, not made, **C.** con - sub - stan - tial with the Fa - ther;

8

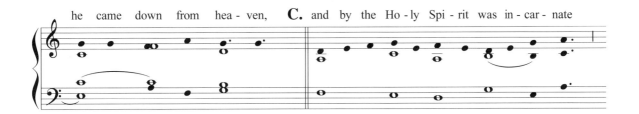

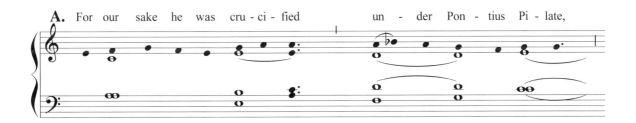

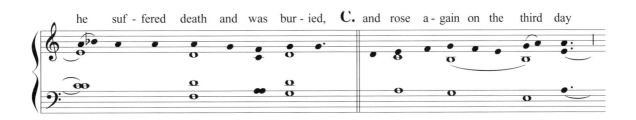

9

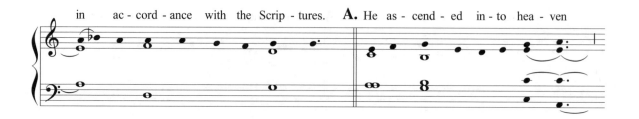

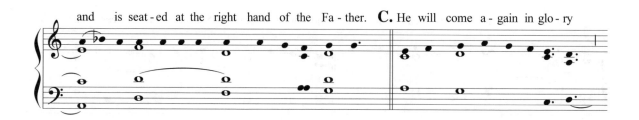

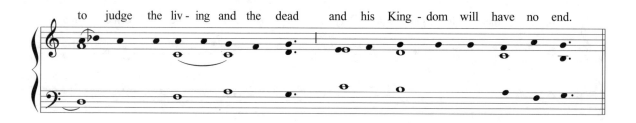

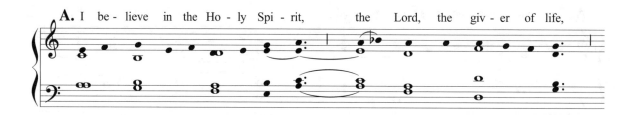

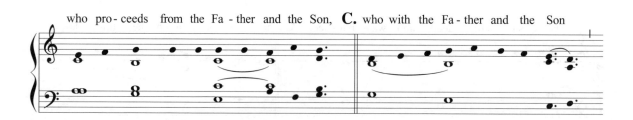

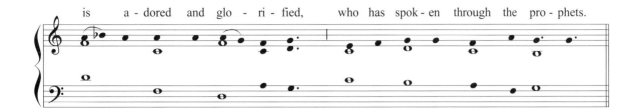

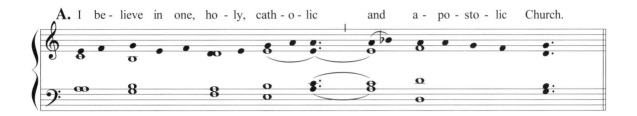

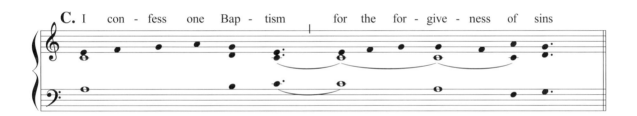

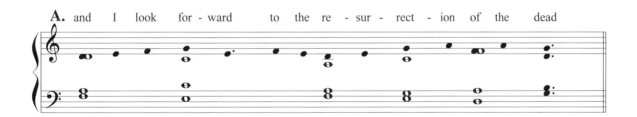

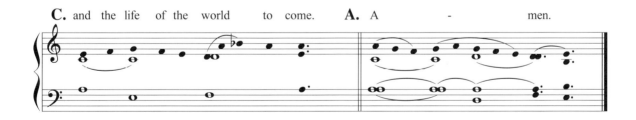

Credo III
(English)

Text and melody: ICEL

Accompaniment by
Geoffrey Cox

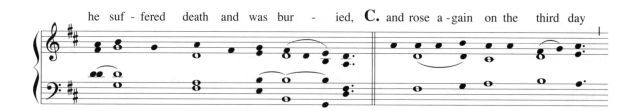

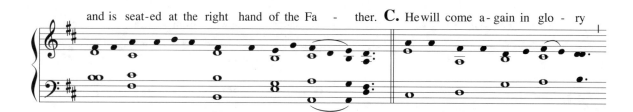

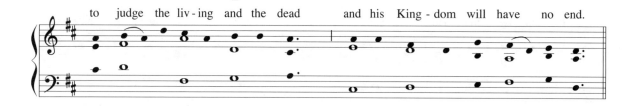

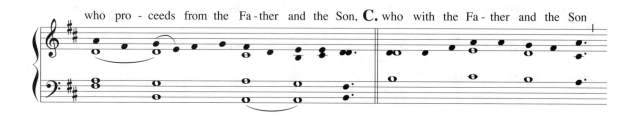

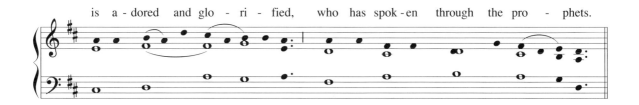

is a - dored and glo - ri - fied, who has spok - en through the pro - phets.

A. And one, ho - ly, cath - o - lic and a - po - sto - lic Church.

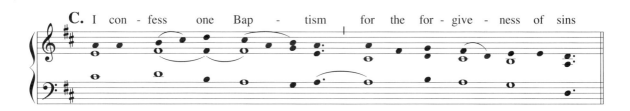

C. I con - fess one Bap - tism for the for - give - ness of sins

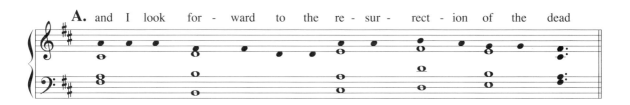

A. and I look for - ward to the re - sur - rect - ion of the dead

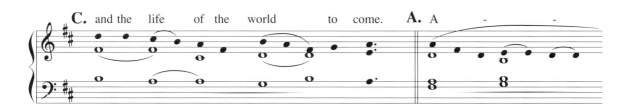

C. and the life of the world to come. **A.** A - -

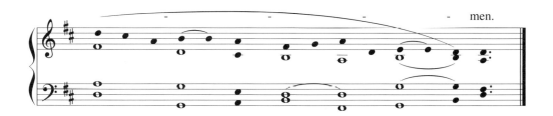

- - - men.

15

Credo III
(Latin)

Melody: 17th century

Accompaniment by
Geoffrey Cox

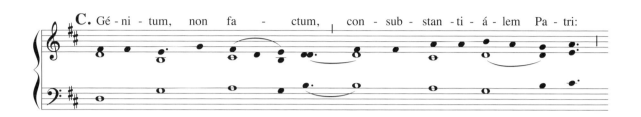

C. Gé - ni - tum, non fa - ctum, con - sub - stan - ti - á - lem Pa - tri:

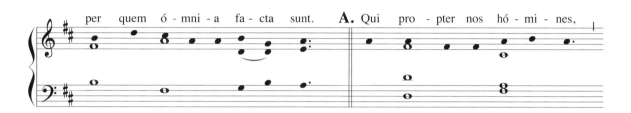

per quem ó - mni - a fa - cta sunt. A. Qui pro - pter nos hó - mi - nes,

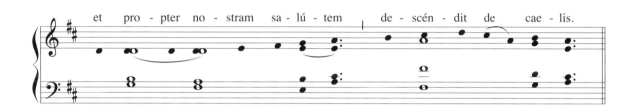

et pro - pter no - stram sa - lú - tem de - scén - dit de cae - lis.

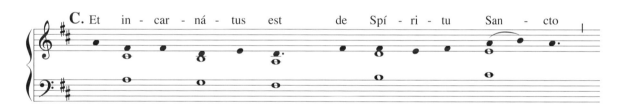

C. Et in - car - ná - tus est de Spí - ri - tu San - cto

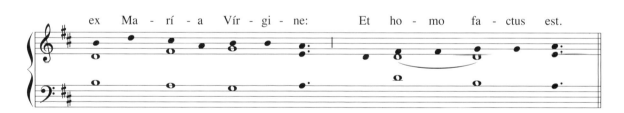

ex Ma - rí - a Vír - gi - ne: Et ho - mo fa - ctus est.

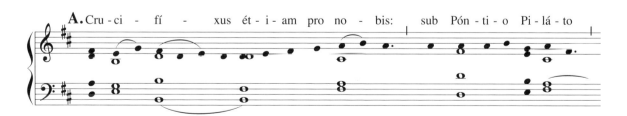

A. Cru - ci - fí - xus ét - i - am pro no - bis: sub Pón - ti - o Pi - lá - to

17

pas - sus, et se - púl - tus est. **C.** Et res - sur - ré - xit tér - ti - a di - e,

se - cún - dum Scri - ptú - ras. **A.** Et a - scén - dit in cae - lum:

se - det ad déx - te - ram Pa - tris. **C.** Et í - te - rum ven - tú - rus est cum gló - ri - a,

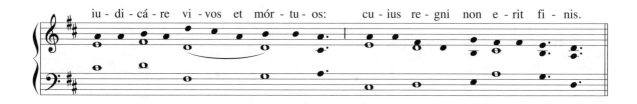

iu - di - cá - re vi - vos et mór - tu - os: cu - ius re - gni non e - rit fi - nis.

A. Et in Spí - ri - tum San - ctum, Do - mi - num, et vi - vi - fi - cán - tem:

qui ex Pa - tre Fi - li - ó - que pro - cé - dit. **C.** Qui cum Pa - tre et Fí - li - o

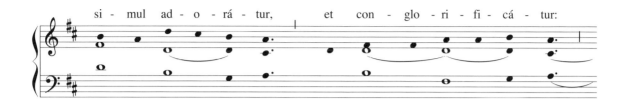

si - mul ad - o - rá - tur, et con - glo - ri - fi - cá - tur:

qui lo - cú - tus est per Pro - phé - tas. **A.** Et u - nam san - ctam ca - thó - li - cam

et a - po - stó - li - cam Ec - clé - si - am. **C.** Con - fí - te - or u - num ba - ptís - ma

in re - mis - si - ó - nem pec - ca - tó - rum. **A.** Et ex - spé - cto re - sur - re - cti -

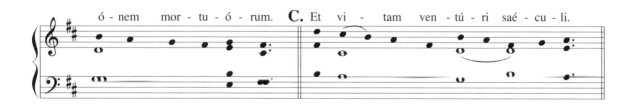

ó - nem mor - tu - ó - rum. **C.** Et vi - tam ven - tú - ri saé - cu - li.

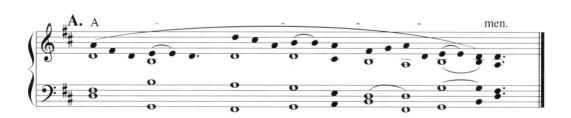

A. A - - - - men.

19

Prayer of the Faithful

Text and melodies: ICEL

Accompaniment by
Geoffrey Cox

The text that follows the dagger (†) in the invocations given
below can also be used to conclude intentions that are not sung.

A.

B.

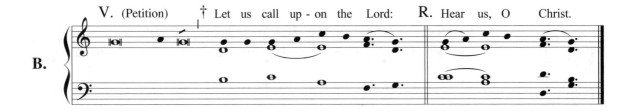

C.

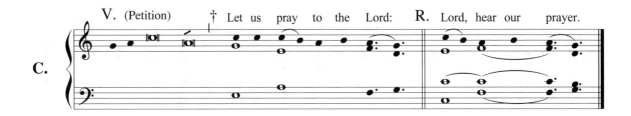

or

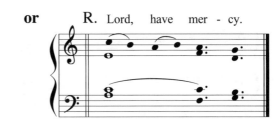

D.

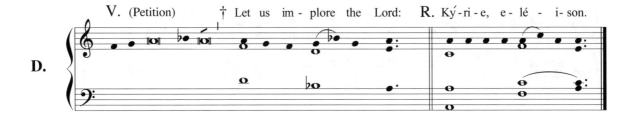

The Eucharistic Prayer

Text and melody: ICEL

Accompaniment by
Geoffrey Cox

Preface Dialogue

Preface

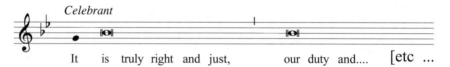

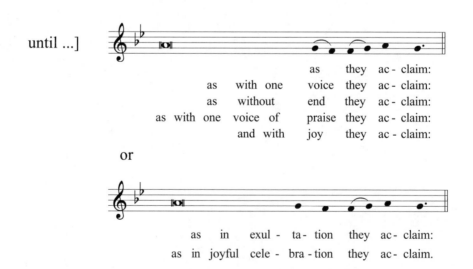

Sanctus XVIII
(English)

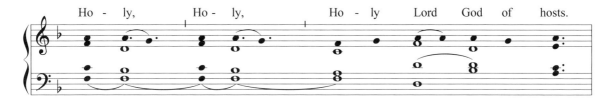

Ho - ly, Ho - ly, Ho - ly Lord God of hosts.

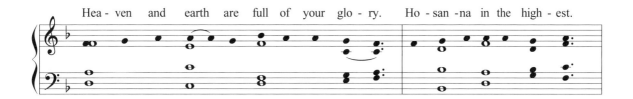

Hea - ven and earth are full of your glo - ry. Ho - san - na in the high - est.

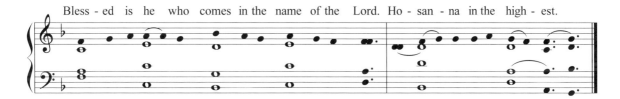

Bless - ed is he who comes in the name of the Lord. Ho - san - na in the high - est.

OR
Sanctus XVIII
(Latin)

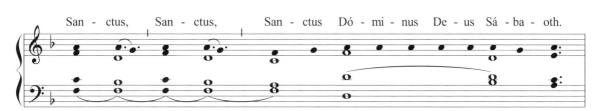

San - ctus, San - ctus, San - ctus Dó - mi - nus De - us Sá - ba - oth.

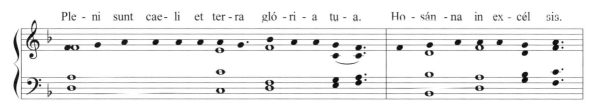

Ple - ni sunt cae - li et ter - ra gló - ri - a tu - a. Ho - sán - na in ex - cél - sis.

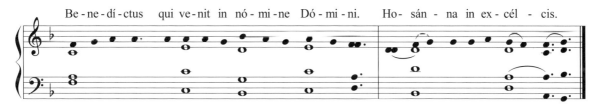

Be - ne - dí - ctus qui ve - nit in nó - mi - ne Dó - mi - ni. Ho - sán - na in ex - cél - cis.

Memorial Acclamation

Celebrant

The my - ste - ry of faith.

No. 1

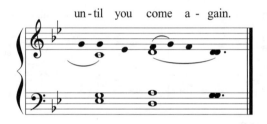

We pro - claim your Death, O Lord, and pro - fess your Re - sur - rec - tion

un - til you come a - gain.

No. 2

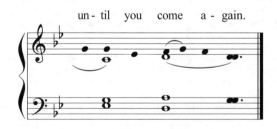

When we eat this Bread and drink this Cup, we pro - claim your Death, O Lord,

un - til you come a - gain.

Save us, Saviour of the world, for by your Cross and Re-sur-rec-tion

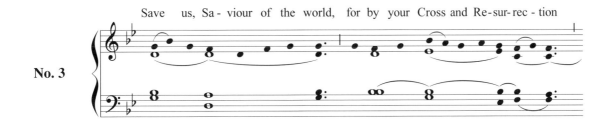

No. 3

you have set us free.

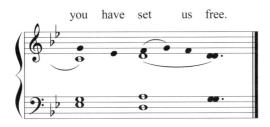

Doxology and Great Amen

Celebrant

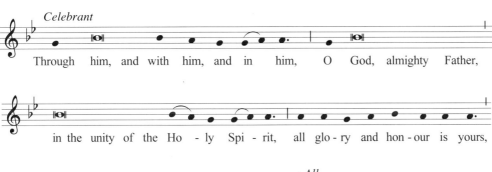

Through him, and with him, and in him, O God, almighty Father,

in the unity of the Ho - ly Spi - rit, all glo - ry and hon - our is yours,

All

for ev - er and ev - er. A - men.

The Lord's Prayer

Text and melody: ICEL

Accompaniment by
Geoffrey Cox

Tone A
(English)

Celebrant

At the Saviour's com - mand and formed by di - vine teach - ing, we dare to say:

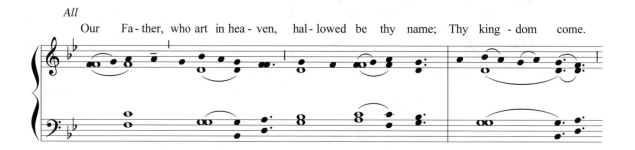

All

Our Fa - ther, who art in hea - ven, hal - lowed be thy name; Thy king - dom come.

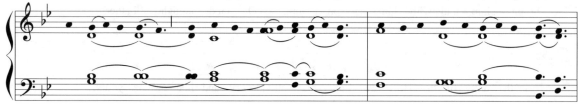

Thy will be done on earth as it is in hea - ven. Give us this day our dai - ly bread,

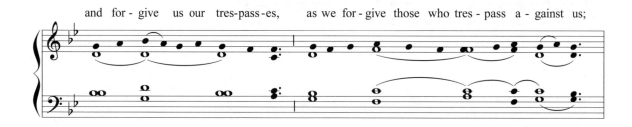

and for - give us our tres-pass -es, as we for - give those who tres - pass a - gainst us;

and lead us not in-to temp-ta - tion, but de-li - ver us from e - vil.

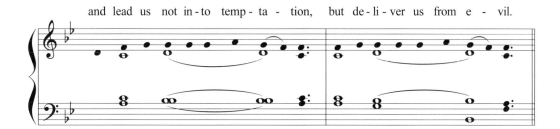

Embolism

Celebrant

De - liver us, Lord, we pray, from every e - vil, graciously grant peace in our days,

that, by the help of your mercy, we may be always free from sin and safe from all dis-tress,

as we a-wait the bless -ed hope and the coming of our Sa - viour, Je-sus Christ.

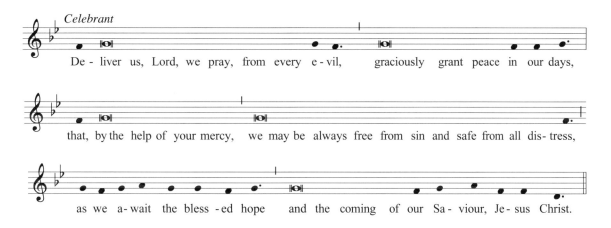

Doxology

All

For the king-dom, the power and the glo - ry are yours now and for ev-er.

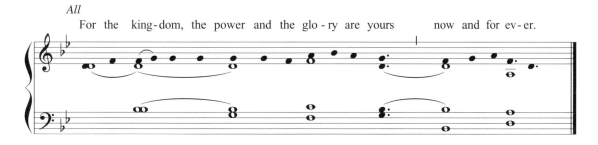

Tone B
(Mozarabic)

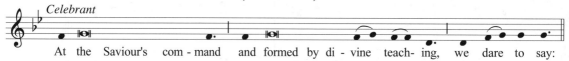

Celebrant

At the Saviour's com-mand and formed by di-vine teach-ing, we dare to say:

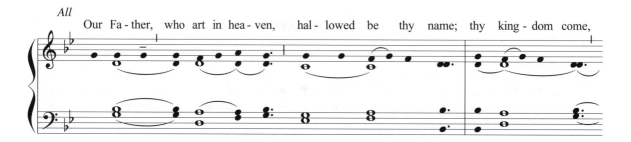

All

Our Fa-ther, who art in hea-ven, hal-lowed be thy name; thy king-dom come,

thy will be done on earth as it is in hea-ven. Give us this day our dai-ly bread,

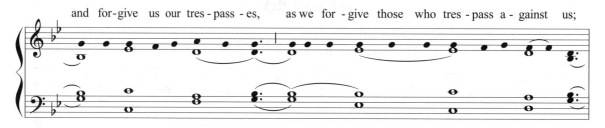

and for-give us our tres-pass-es, as we for-give those who tres-pass a-gainst us;

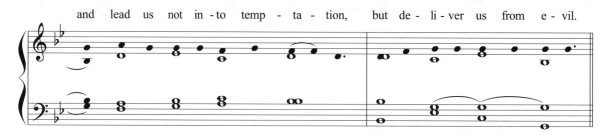

and lead us not in-to temp-ta-tion, but de-li-ver us from e-vil.

**Embolism and Doxology
as for Tone A: see page 27.**

Tone C

(Solemn Anaphora Tone)

Celebrant

At the Saviour's com - mand and formed by di - vine teach - ing, we dare to say:

All

Our Fa - ther, who art in hea - ven, hal - lowed be thy name; thy king - dom come,

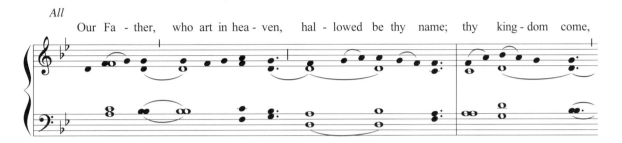

thy will be done on earth as it is in hea - ven. Give us this day our dai - ly bread,

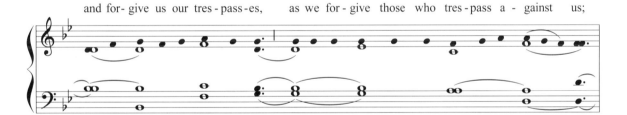

and for - give us our tres - pass - es, as we for - give those who tres - pass a - gainst us;

and lead us not in - to temp - ta - tion, but de - li - ver us from e - vil.

> **Embolism and Doxology
> as for Tone A: see page 27.**

Tone A
(Latin)

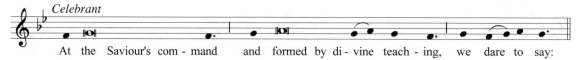

Celebrant

At the Saviour's com - mand and formed by di - vine teach - ing, we dare to say:

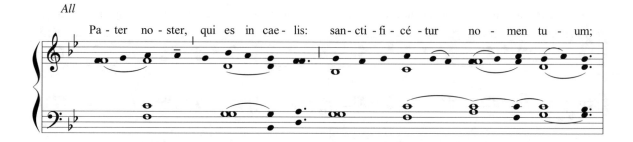

All

Pa - ter no - ster, qui es in cae - lis: san - cti - fi - cé - tur no - men tu - um;

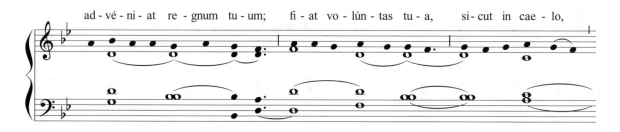

ad - vé - ni - at re - gnum tu - um; fi - at vo - lún - tas tu - a, si - cut in cae - lo,

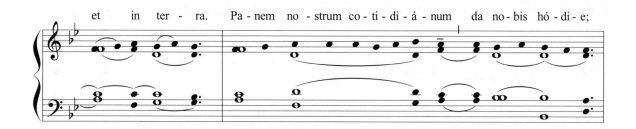

et in ter - ra. Pa - nem no - strum co - ti - di - á - num da no - bis hó - di - e;

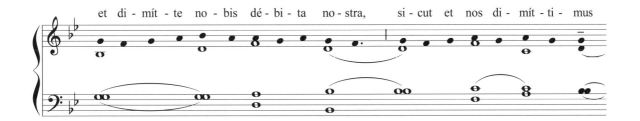

et di - mít - te no - bis dé - bi - ta no - stra, si - cut et nos di - mít - ti - mus

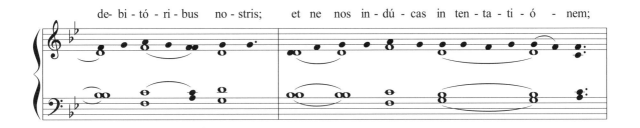

de - bi - tó - ri - bus no - stris; et ne nos in - dú - cas in ten - ta - ti - ó - nem;

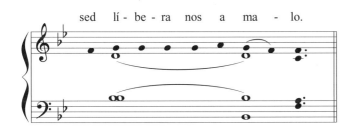

sed lí - be - ra nos a ma - lo.

Embolism and Doxology
as for Tone A (English):
see page 27.

Agnus Dei XVIII

(English)

Text and melody: ICEL

Accompaniment by
Geoffrey Cox

Lamb of God, you take a-way the sins of the world, have mer-cy on us.

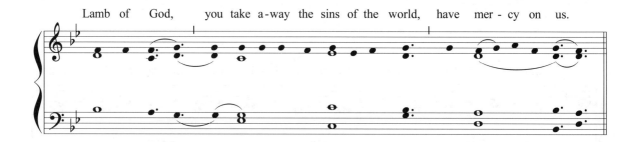

Lamb of God, you take a-way the sins of the world, have mer-cy on us.

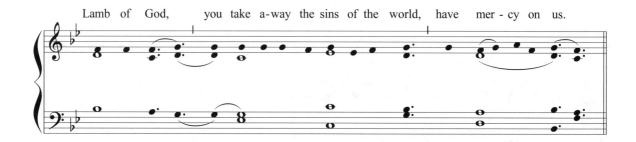

Lamb of God, you take a-way the sins of the world, grant us peace.

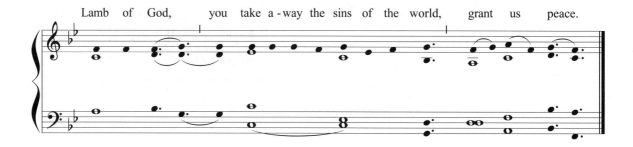

Agnus Dei XVIII
(Latin)

Melody: 12th Century

Accompaniment by
Geoffrey Cox

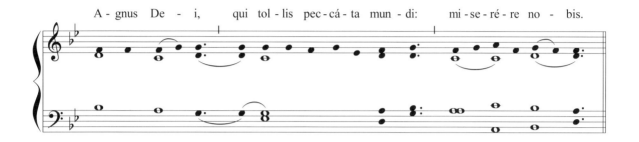

A - gnus De - i, qui tol - lis pec - cá - ta mun - di: mi - se - ré - re no - bis.

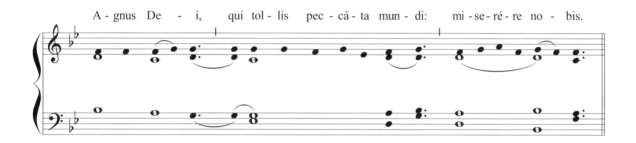

A - gnus De - i, qui tol - lis pec - cá - ta mun - di: mi - se - ré - re no - bis.

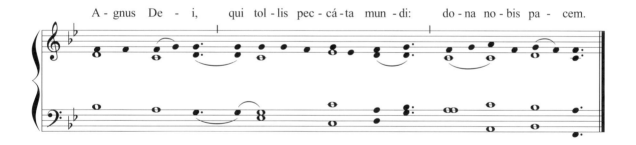

A - gnus De - i, qui tol - lis pec - cá - ta mun - di: do - na no - bis pa - cem.

33